Bold Baron Osbert

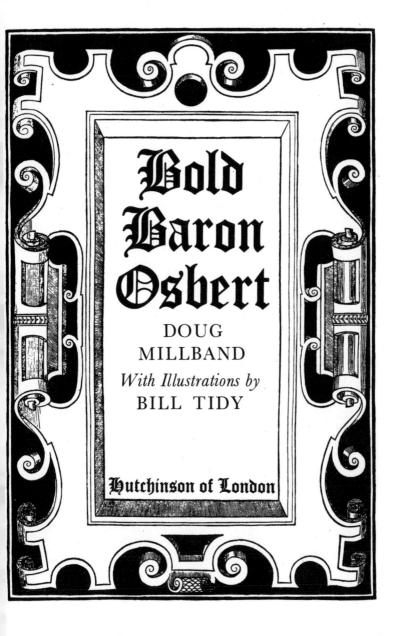

Bold Baron Osbert

DOUG
MILLBAND

With Illustrations by
BILL TIDY

Hutchinson of London

08551587
03055894
L00032096X

HUTCHINSON & CO (*Publishers*) LTD
3 Fitzroy Square, London W1

London Melbourne Sydney Auckland
Wellington Johannesburg Cape Town
and agencies throughout the world

First published 1972

Text © Doug Millband 1972
Illustrations © Bill Tidy 1972

*This book has been set in Monophoto Baskerville,
by Oliver Burridge Filmsetting Ltd., Crawley, Sussex,
printed in Great Britain by Flarepath Printers Ltd.,
St. Albans, Herts. and bound by Wm. Brendon & Son,
of Tiptree, Essex*

ISBN 0 09 113531 1

For Betty, Debbie, Nicola and Gary,
and with thanks also to Barry Askew,
who lit the fuse.

Contents

I

Osbert is demobbed
from the Crusades

I'll tell you a tale of historical note,
Let me see now, when would it be?
It were long before Nelson and Cromwell
About twelve hundred and three.
There lived a bold Baron called Osbert
In a castle, way out on a moor.
He hadn't a car or a telly
On account of his being so poor.
His vassals and serfs had deserted
And Osbert had said to his spouse,
'If things don't improve by the winter,
We'll try for a council house.
This castle's a terrible burden
It costs me a fortune to keep.
At six bob a month for the mortgage,
You have to agree, it's not cheap.'

Well, early one morning that winter
The Baron awoke about eight,
To a thunderous hollering and shouting
By a bloke on his horse at the gate.
The Baron went over to t'window
Shoved his head and his shoulders through
And looking down onto the horseman,
He shouted, 'Whatever's to do?'
The horseman looked up at the Baron
And putting his hand in his coat,
He shouted, 'I've browt thee a letter,
Wouldst tha mind dropping t'bridge o'er t'moat?'
The Baron thought, 'By gum, that's funny,
I wonder who's writing to me.
I'll bet half a crown it's a summons.
Still, I'd better get down there and see.'

He threw an old coat o'er his nightie
And with an incredible din,
He pulled up t'portcullis, dropped t'drawbridge
And th'horseman come galloping in.
Said th' horseman, 'Art tha known as Osbert?'
Osbert said, 'Aye lad, that's me.
If tha's come about th'H.P. on t'cooker,
I'll pay it next week lad, tha'll see.'
The horseman dismounted and answered,
'About cookers I don't know a thing.
I've just come up th'M6 from London
To fetch thee a note from the King.'
He handed the Baron a letter,
Which he pulled from inside his string vest.
It were yellowed and curled at the edges
And stamped with the royal crest.

The Baron ripped open the letter
And read through the lines in a tick,
'Odds bodkins!' he cried, 'It's mi callup.
I'm going off to war wi' King Dick.'
Osbert's wife had come down from the boudoir
To see what the fuss was about
And as she stepped into the courtyard
She heard the last part of this shout.
'Does this mean tha's got paid employment?'
The Baron said, 'Aye lass, that's true.
I'll make a few bob spearing arabs
And perhaps win a medal or two.'
Said his wife, 'Well, I'd best get thi armour,
There's no point in any delay.
The sooner tha gets to thi unit
The sooner they'll send me your pay.'

So she fetched it from out of the wardrobe
It were dented and starting to rust
Feathers on th'helmet had moulted
And t'scabbard were bunged up wi'dust.
He had quite a job to get in it.
'Ee it's tight lass,' he said with a grunt.
'That isn't surprising' said th'horseman,
'You've got the damn thing back to front.'
But at last the Bold Baron was ready
And kissing his wife on the cheek
He said, 'Well, we'd better get going
I'll write to you sometime next week.
I'll get them to send thi mi wages
To pay the electricity bill
And when I get back from the frontline
We'll go for a fortnight to Rhyl.'

And then the pair rode off o'er t'drawbridge
And didn't look back anymore,
While Osbert's wife checked his insurance
To find out how much she might draw.

Baron Osbert was gone for a decade
His castle fell into decay
They cut off the gas and th'electric
And t'bailiff took t'cooker away.
Things didn't look too good for th'owd lady
But, being a right loyal spouse
She ran off to Blackpool wi' t'rentman
When he promised a new council house.

It were one Friday night the next autumn
When Osbert rode up to the moat
His left leg in plaster, one arm in a sling
And six medals pinned to his coat.

He found the portcullis wide open
And he knew there were summat amiss
For the dustbins had never been emptied
And his wife wasn't there with a kiss.
A ragged old crone gathered firewood
By the side of the crumbling west gate.
'If you're seeking your wife my lord Baron
I'm afraid that tha's come home too late.
She waited and waited for ages
Now brace thisen lad for a shock,
She's run off to Blackpool wi' t'rentman
And opened a shop selling rock.'

So Osbert rode straight up to Blackpool
And booked in at digs for the week,
Run by a woman called Grundy
With whiskers and scar on her cheek.
Said the woman, 'Now no gallivanting,
I'd best have your rent in advance.
I don't allow horses in t'bedrooms
And don't scratch the paint wi' your lance.'
Baron Osbert thought nowt to his bedroom
'T would have given a midget the cramp
The walls were alive wi' green fungus
And the bedding were mouldy and damp.
But he'd propped up his lance in the wardrobe
Hung his armour on t'back of the door,
When the hook came away from the woodwork
And his breastplate went straight through the floor.

Mrs. Grundy called Osbert a vandal
And threatened to call in the law.
Unless he paid over a tenner
And patched up the hole in the floor.
Osbert hadn't much choice in the matter
He felt he was out on a limb
You can't really batter a woman
And besides, she was bigger than him.
Baron Osbert was never a coward
But that evening, soon after dark
He crept out of t'digs wi' his baggage
And went and kipped down in the park.
'Well, there's one thing, at least it's not raining,'
Said Osbert, 'that's one bit of luck.'
But he soon changed his mind about midnight
When a deluging thunderstorm struck.

The next morning dawned bright and sunny
With blue skies and clouds white as cream
As Osbert rode off up the seafront
Enrobed in a large cloud of steam.
He started his search up at Cleveleys
And worked his way down to the pier
But having had no luck by lunchtime
He knocked off and went for a beer.
He found a nice pub by the tower
It stood at the end of a block
Next to an automat blacksmiths
And a quaint little shop selling rock.

Thought the Baron, 'I'll just check on this one,
Before I go into the pub,
Odds bodkins, this place looks revolting,
I'll just give this window a rub.'
So he rubbed at the glass with his hankie
And shoved his nose up to the pane
And there, at the back of the counter
Was the Bold Baron's wife, Lady Jane.

'Gadzooks lass it's thee,' quoth the Baron,
But the good lady gave out a wail
At th'armour clad vision at t'window
In breastplate and rusting chain mail.
Osbert crept in rather sheepish,
He knew that he'd given her a fright
For her hair was stood up like a mop head
And the rock in her hand had turned white.
All at once Lady Jane had hysterics,
'It's a ghost, it's a spook, you're not real.'
To which Baron Osbert said, 'Knickers!—
I'm really quite solid, just feel.'
But his missus were still a bit cautious
From having just had such a shock
And reaching towards him oer t'counter
She gave him a poke with the rock.

'I told you, you barmpot,' said Osbert,
'Whatever put that in your head?
I've never felt better for ages,
So what made you think I was dead?'
'What else could I think' asked his missus
Her eyes brimming full of salt tears
I naturally thought you'd got nobbled
When I don't see your face for ten years.
You ne'er sent a note and no money
Or let me know you were alright.'
To which Osbert answered, 'I'm sorry,
We didn't get much time to write.'
Said his missus, 'Well what's the position?
I've managed to save a few bob
And I'm not going back to yon castle
Unless you can find a good job.'

Baron Osbert thought hard for a moment.
'That's enough of this nonsense,' said he,
'After I've trailed all t'way up to Blackpool
You're coming back home lass, with me.'
'I've got twenty quid from the army,
It's enough to buy victuals and coal
And as for some sort of employment
I'll soon get fixed up on the dole.'
And so Lady Jane had relented
And sold the rock shop to a Jew
For three hundred pounds, rock included
And five thousand paper bags, too.
So then the pair rode back to Bolton
As the sun sank away in the west
With Jane behind Osbert on t'saddle,
Hanging on for grim life to his vest.

They got back to t'castle next morning
To a scene of neglect and decay
For the castle had suffered some hardship
While t'Baron and Jane were away
There were big pieces missing from t'drawbridge
T'portcullis were rusted and brown
And it hung there like, sort of lopsided
Neither all the way up nor right down.
The whole place was cloaked in damp silence
A blanket of mist on the ground
And but for the Baron's knees knocking
There wasn't as much as a sound.
They crept round the side of the courtyard
First Osbert, then Jane, then the steed
In case they should meet some fierce dragon
That had taken up refuge in t'weed.

'You hang on out here,' hissed the Baron
As into the hallway he trod.
'Not likely, mate' answered his missus
I'm not staying out here on mi todd.'
Osbert's horse shared the lady's opinion,
Thinking, 'I'm not just here for the ride,
So don't think you're leaving me matey,
I'm following you two inside.'
The inside of the hall were a shambles
In thick dust and cobwebs bedecked
Someone had set fire to the curtains
And the Baron's best chair had been wrecked.
The sideboard were all scratched and splintered
And covered in candlewax drips
Whilst piled in a heap by the fireplace
Were beer cans and bags of cold chips.

It looked like an army of Cossacks
Had kipped for the night in the hall
And some one had sprayed 'Up United'
In tartan red paint down the wall.
Well this was the final insult
It brought Lady Jane close to tears
For both Lady Jane and the Baron
Had watched Preston North End for years.
'Do you think it was hippies?' asked Janey
'I've heard that they're not very neat.'
To which Osbert gave her an answer
In words that I dare not repeat.
It took them some time to get shipshape
But at last the old place looked quite nice,
'Is there owt left in t'pantry' asked Osbert,
'Or has it been scoffed by the mice?'

There were four cans of beans and some celery
A small tin of button mushrooms
A half bag of lentils, some sago
And a packet of rancid dried prunes.
'That's not very much,' said the Baron,
'Still Janey, see what you can do.
Just shove the whole lot in the cauldron
It might make a passable stew.'
The smell from the brew was revolting
As it foamed to the top of the brim
Osbert's horse fled outside in a panic,
He thought that they'd made it for him.
Of course, the mess couldn't be eaten,
Said the Baron, 'So much for the stew.
It's a pity to waste it though, Janey,
It should make a pretty stout glue.'

They were lucky and found a few crackers,
A stale crust and half a scotch bap,
And Lady Jane got quite excited,
When she found some cheese rind in a trap.
Said Osbert, 'Well, roll on tomorrow,
I think that the first thing to do
Is to go to our Fred's in St. Helens
Their Lill makes a great Irish stew.
Then we'll stock up wi' goodies in Bolton
And get them to bring us some coal
Which should see us through for the meantime
Until I get fixed up on t'dole.
Then he gave Jane a kiss on her earhole,
'I've been away ten years' he said,
'And I'm right glad I'm back wi' you Janey,
Let's get up them stairs into bed.'

2

Revenge is sweet—
or a tight spot for the rentman

The last time we heard of the Baron
Not to mention his wife, Lady Jane.
They'd come back to t'castle on t'moor
Determined to start life again
They hadn't much cash in the kitty
Though Janey had saved a few bob,
Which kept them in t'manner accustomed
While Osbert looked out for a job.
He'd been down to t'dole place in Bolton
And joined on the end of a queue,
Along with twelve tough Irish labourers
And a big crowd of immigrants too.
They offered him a job on a stagecoach
Though Osbert thought nowt of the pay,
Sat at the back of six horses
And getting wet through every day.

There was work to be had by the Mersey
As a labourer down on the docks
If he fancied a move up to Preston
They wanted a keeper for t'stocks.
Said Osbert, 'Nay, have you nowt local?
There must be all sorts I could do.
How about being a sales rep,
Wi' expenses and company horse too.'
But they had nowt at all that would suit him
So back to the castle he went
Wondering how he'd make some wages
And how he could muster the rent.
Osbert's wife were stood waiting on t'drawbridge
A telegram form in her hand,
Thought Osbert, 'By Gad, I've been re-called,
Things must be bad in th'Holy Land.'

'Ee Osbert,' cried Jane, all excited,
'I've got some right good news for you.
You've been picked to go jousting for England
At t'grand jousting meeting at Crewe.'
'You what?' cried the Baron, 'you're joking,'
As he grabbed the buff form from her hand,
'Gad, you're right, and it's signed by Alf Ramsey.
But why me?—I don't understand.'
'He must have been watching in t'desert
When we beat Saladin all ends up.
I thought that I saw him in t'grandstand
When King Dick went up to get t'cup.'
So Osbert and Jane had a party
On account of this wonderful news
With roast sucking pig and fish fingers
And some of Jane's home prepared booze.

Osbert's prospects were looking quite rosy
For jousters he knew, got good pay
And he might get a job on the telly
Reporting on 'Joust of the Day'.
So he sharpened his lance and his broadsword
And had his old horse M.O.T.'d
Then he and Jane jumped into t'saddle
And set off for Crewe at top speed.
The crowds down in Crewe were fantastic,
For this joust were England v.' t'rest,
Wi' t'Jocks and the Micks and the Taffies
All shouting that their lot were best
The pubs were packed out to the doorways
The punters were placing their bets,
While th'hawkers were making a fortune
Selling hamburgers, chips and rosettes.

Jane and Osbert met up wi' Alf Ramsey
Along wi' the rest of the team,
A right regal bunch of top jousters,
The absolute pick of the cream.
There was Lord Ethelbert of Tintagel
Oscar the vicious from Stoke,
And Athelstein Fitzroy of Bootle
A real hard case of a bloke.
'Right,' Alf said, 'now for the tactics.
It's a pity we've not got Geoff Hurst
He's gone down with lurgy they tell me,
So Osbert will have to go first.
You know the score don't you now, Ossie,
We've got to get straight through their ranks,
If they start trying to pull the offside trap,
Just nip round the back on their flanks.'

The kick off were set for two-thirty
On account of the long winter nights
If extra time had to be called for,
They'd finish it off under t'lights.
The ground was packed out, full to bustin',
The crowd full of meat pie and beer,
As Osbert took up his position
To the sound of a thunderous cheer.
Now Osbert were nifty at lancing
And jousting were right in his line
He'd upended four Jocks and three Taffies
When t'ref's whistle went for half time.
But his team-mates had had quite a struggle,
Opponents weren't playing t'game fair
There'd been hacking and pushing and tripping
And t'score at half time were all square.

The joust carried on for some hours
And neither side managed to score
Till, with only five minutes to t'whistle
The crowd were convinced of a draw.
Baron Osbert had t'last go for England
His opponent he'd have to unseat
If he mistimed his run he were snookered
And England could well face defeat.
His opponent were dressed in red armour,
Four feathers on th'helmet in black,
A haggis in white on his breastplate
And 'Home Rule for Scotland' on t'back.
Thought the Baron, 'Yon bloke looks familiar,
I remember yon big piebald horse,
I've seen it back home at the castle—
It's Cedric, the rentman—of course!'

'I thowt it were thee,' cried the Baron
'I'll show you the way to behave,
Stand by to get skewered, you scoundrel
Say your prayers, you adulterous knave.'
Now Cedric the rentman were shaken,
He could see that the outlook were bad.
'Now 'old on a minute' he answered,
'Let's not get too hasty owd lad.'
'Just cut out the cackle,' bawled Osbert
'I'll teach you to mess wi' my Jane,
By the time that I've finished wi' you mate,
You'll not bother ladies again.'
The crowd sensed the needle between them
And a hush of expectancy fell
'Guard your goodies, you cad,' shouted Osbert
And Cedric replied, 'You as well!'

They each had a tilt at the other
But neither one scored a bulls eye
And the match had gone into t'last minute
As they lined up to have one last try.
It were just then that fate played her trump card
For as Osbert's horse thundered by,
A bloke in the crowd pitched the remnants
Of a piece of his mum's apple pie.
Well, what happened next were spectacular.
Osbert's horse were quite partial to cakes
And when he espied this choice morsel
The old stead slapped on all its brakes.
Osbert shot through the air like an arrow
As Cedric bore down on his foe.
Lady Jane hid her head in her handbag
And Alf Ramsey cried out, 'Oh no!'

But fate hadn't finished with Osbert,
Though the crowd thought he'd had his last chance
But they'd reckoned without Dame good fortune
And the tip of the Bold Baron's lance.
It stuck in the ground before Osbert
And whipped in the air like a lash
Hurling the Baron on Cedric
Who fell to the ground with a crash.
The crowd had never seen nowt like it,
You could hear the roar all over Crewe
As Osbert stood there, astride Cedric
The note of the ref's whistle blew.
They chaired Osbert off like a hero
Said Alf, 'What a trick, how's it done?'
But Osbert were still dazed and breathless
He didn't know England had won!'

It seemed they had problems wi' Cedric
For his armour had got rather bent
And they found that they couldn't remove it
So off to the scrapyard they went.
They started the job about tea time
And finished it off after ten
But due to a slip wi' a chisel,
He won't be the same man again.

3
The Royal Lodger

When Osbert came back from the jousting
He found that he'd made quite a name
He were pestered each day by reporters
To give his account of the game.
He appeared on 'Sportsnight with Coleman'
And did a stint with Stuart Hall
As guest star for Torquay United
When they played Liverpool at Quiz Ball.
Of course this brought in lots of money
Much to the Baron's delight.
For after the long months of struggle
Things seemed to have turned out alright.
He spent every day round the castle
From morning to evening he toiled
Repairing the holes in the drawbridge
And getting the portcullis oiled.

One evening late on in November
The Baron had had a late tea,
And he and his wife, in their nighties,
Had sat down to watch the T.V.
The show were 'The Late Night Thriller'
A spine-chilling tale about spooks
That had the Bold Baron and Janey
Absorbed and on tenterhooks.
'Ee Osbert, this gives me the willies,'
Said Janey, 'How about you?'
'I daren't move away from the fire
And I'm dying to go to the loo.'
Osbert had to stand guard with the poker
While his wife nipped off up the dark stair
'This is ridiculous,' thought Osbert
'As if there'd be ghosties up there.'

The cold wind moaned in through the window
As Osbert stood there in the gloom
Listening to t'wailing and shrieking
From t'telly set in t'other room.
He took a firm grip on the poker
As he felt his flesh starting to creep,
'Where the devil is Janey?' he muttered,
'Has the daft woman dropped off to sleep?'
It must have been nigh twenty minutes
That Osbert stood there in the dark
With his knees knocking under his nightie
Till he muttered, 'Stuff this for a lark!'
'Hey Janey, what's up lass?' he bellowed,
'Are you spending all night in the loo?
'Cause I'm going back to watch t'telly,
Just give us a shout when you're through.'

There wasn't a sound from above him
Baron Osbert thought, 'Gadzooks, that's odd.
She's perhaps passed away in the privvy,
What a rough way to go, the poor sod.'
He crept up the stairs with the poker
To find the loo door open wide
With the moon shining in through the window
But no sign of Janey inside.
There wasn't a sound on the landing
Just the wind moaning under the door
And the drip, dripping noise of the cistern
As it leaked out all over the floor.

Baron Osbert were getting quite jumpy
And felt a temptation to shout
'What the hell's going on?' But he didn't
Then t'candle on t'wall spluttered out.
Osbert froze on the spot like a statue
In the gloom at the top of the stairs,
For the sudden descent into darkness
Had caught the poor chap unawares.
The Baron's teeth started to chatter
He felt his knees start to go weak
As an oak-studded door down the landing
Started opening up with a creak.

'Who is it?' he managed to stutter,
He'd have run but his feet felt like lead,
And the hair on his scalp stood up rigid
And shoved his night cap off his head.
The door opened wider and wider
With Osbert prepared to take flight
As a figure stepped out on the landing
In a long flowing garment of white.
You'd have heard Osbert's shout down in Oldham
'My God! it's a boggart,' he cried,
And he'd gone down ten steps in a second,
And covered six more in a stride.

He were just making tracks for the drawbridge
At a truly incredible rate
When he heard a faint voice shouting 'Osbert!
Just hang on a minute—please—wait!'
Osbert slid to a halt by the gatehouse
'That sounds just like Janey,' he mused
Then he shouted 'Unhand her, foul spirit,
I'll not have my missus abused.'
He raced back inside the old castle
And grabbing his lance from its place
He made for the stairs to the landing
Determined to show a bold face.

'On guard evil spirit,' cried Osbert,
'Stand by, lad, to get thiself speared,'
When the door to the stairway creaked open
And the ghostly clad figure appeared.
Baron Osbert were just going to lance it
When the figure stepped into the light
It were Lady Jane, dressed in her nightie,
Saying, 'Osbert love—are you alright?'
'You bloody great crackpot, yelled Osbert,
On seeing 'the ghost' was his wife,
'Fancy floating about like a boggart,
You gave me the fright of my life.'

'What a daft trick to play,' ranted Osbert,
And Lady Jane started to weep,
'It wasn't a trick I was playing
I heard a noise up in the Keep.'
'It was probably bats' Osbert snorted
His legs shaking still from his fright
'They flutter about up in t'rafters
I've heard em on many a night'

The pair made their way to the landing
And up the stairs started to creep
Until they were stood at the doorway
Which opened up into the Keep.
For a moment they stood in the darkness
The silence could almost be felt,
As Osbert reached down for the key ring
That hung from the front of his belt.
He were just putting t'key into t'keyhole
When Lady Jane hissed in his ear,
'Hey Osbert, I think summat's burning,
Sniff up, can you smell it my dear?'
Osbert sniffed and he said, 'Aye you're right love,
It smells like they're baking to me,
We'll soon put a stop to this nonsense
Let's open this door up and see.'

Osbert opened the door with a flourish,
'Avast there, ye varlets,' he cried.
Then he stopped in his tracks in amazement
For the place was deserted inside.
A big fire were burning in t'fireplace
The table was set out for tea
Wi' three chairs, a bench and a telly
But no one that Osbert could see.
Lady Jane stuck her head round the door hole
She could see there was nobody there
'They've perhaps nipped outside,' she suggested
To get a quick breath of fresh air.'
'Don't talk like a twerp' answered Osbert
Still casting a glance all around
'Unless they went out through the window,
And we're two hundred feet from the ground.

'I can see what was burning!' cried Janey,
'Look over there on the hob.
Some one's been making some rock cakes
And made a pig's ear of the job.'
The buns were all blackened and smoking
Osbert wrinkled his nose at the stench
And grabbing the tray with his hankie
He put the buns down on the bench.
The couple stood there feeling puzzled
Then Osbert said, 'By gum, it's queer.
The door's locked, and yet the room's empty,
There's summat strange going on here.'
He went o'er and looked through the window
While Janey held t'poker real tight
She was certain that something would happen
And what's more, the Lady was right.

All at once, in the gloom of the corner,
A strange shape began to appear,
And a voice, sort of hollow and distant
Said, 'What the hell's going on here?'
Lady Jane gave a great cry and fainted
At this vision so ghastly and weird
And Osbert stuck, halfway through t'window
As an odd looking figure appeared.
It was dressed in a funny brown garment
Tied round the waist wi' some string
A crown on its head, full of jewels
And on its right hand a big ring.
It was holding a big bag of sugar
Some milk and a bottle of hock.
And a copy of Jimmy Young's cookbook
Were stuck down the front of its frock.

That this was a ghost was quite certain
And Osbert was chilled to the core,
But he daren't make a quick dash for freedom
And leave Lady Jane on the floor.
He mustered up all of his courage
Though his nerves felt like bits of fine wire.
'And who might you be?' Osbert queried
'What seekest thou, might I enquire?'
'My name is King Alfred,' said t'vision,
I seem to have shocked you I fear.
But I merely asked you a question,
What the devil you're doing in here.'
'We happen to live here,' snapped Osbert
'And I don't recall signing your lease,
So you'd best sling your hook rather sharpish
Or I'll nip down and send for the police.'

'You mean, it's your house then?' said Alfred,
'I'm terribly sorry old friend.
It were empty and falling to bits like.
We thought the place must be condemned.'
'Who's we?' Osbert asked, all suspicious,
'Are there more of you living in t'place.
I'll not have my home like a doss house,
What a cheek, what a thundering disgrace.
I like to be fair,' he continued,
'I think that I'm fairer than most.
But I'd rather be lumbered with hippies
Than give open house to a ghost.'
'That's not very kind,' said King Alfred,
'We're really no trouble at all.
We don't need a key to the castle,
We'll come in and out through the wall.'

'You really won't know we are presen
We'd be happy to work for our keep.
We tried to find digs down in Bolton
But we couldn't find good lodgings cheap.'
It was clear that the ghost wasn't evil
In fact he appeared a good sort.
So Osbert relaxed and then answered,
'Alright then, I'll give it some thought.'
Lady Jane were still flaked out near t'fireplace.
Said Alf, 'What's to do wi' your spouse?
She seems to have kipped down on t'hearthrug
Have you not got a bed in the house?
'You caused her to faint,' answered Osbert.
'She's not used to ghosties like you.
I'd best fetch a glass of cold water
And see if I can't bring her too.'

'Let her smell something strong' said King Alfred,
'That ought to get her on her feet.'
Said the Baron, 'Just pass us a rock bun,
I reckon that might work a treat.'
Osbert held out the bun to her nostrils
Then waited while things took their course
And suddenly Jane sat bolt upright
As if she'd been kicked by a horse.
'What's happened?' enquired the old lady,
'What on earth was that horrible thing?
I've never seen owt so repulsive!'
'There's no need for rudeness,' said t'King.
'You're no portrait,' King Alfred continued,
It was clear he was getting annoyed,
'I've seen better legs on a camel,
And we had to have that one destroyed.'

Baron Osbert took charge of t'proceedings,
'Now let's not get childish,' said he.
'There's no need for bickering and insults
So both of you listen to me.'
He explained to his wife about Alfred
That his missus was frightened was plain
But seeing that Osbert weren't bothered
She decided she'd not faint again.
'So you're looking for lodgings,' she queried
'What price are you willing to pay?
We could offer a bed and your breakfast
For something like four pence a day.'
'It's a deal,' cried King Alfred, delighted,
'That seems like a bargain to me.
I'll just give a shout for the others,
But I'm sure that they're bound to agree.'

'Alright lads, let's have you,' cried Alfred,
In a voice that made Lady Jane quake,
And a voice in the distance said, 'Knickers!
We don't want a piece of your cake.'
'Get yourselves down here' bawled Alfred
'I won't stand for telling you twice'
When he threatened to make them eat t'rock buns
Four figures appeared in a trice.
'Ah, there you are lads,' said King Alfred.
'Now Baron, might I introduce
The ghosts of King Harold of Hastings,
Prince Rupert, and Robert the Bruce.
The one on the end in the cassock
Is known to the lads as 'Sir Fred''
Then, dropping his voice to a whisper,
'The poor bloke keeps losing his head.'
The newcomers bowed to the Baron
And then bowed towards Lady Jane.
But Sir Fred's head fell off on t'carpet
And Lady Jane fainted again.

And so Lady Jane and the Baron
Spent that winter at t'castle on t'moor
Wi' a regular income from t'lodgers
To help keep the wolf from the door.
They had a wild party at Christmas
And another the same at New Year
Wi' singsongs and games wi' the ghosties
And gallons of Lady Jane's beer.
Life, it seemed, were a bed of sweet roses
And the battles and hardships were past
A calm and contented existence
Had reached Osbert's castle at last!